Twenty-six Princesses

DAVE HOROWITZ

SCHOLASTIC INC.
New York Toronto London Auckland Sydney
Mexico City New Delhi Hong Kong Buenos Aires

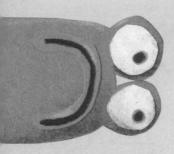

For my brother, Rob

BIBLIOGRAPHY: Dunkling, Leslie, and William Gosling. *The New American Dictionary of Baby Names.* New York: Signet, 1983.

ISBN-13: 978-0-545-20410-1
ISBN-10: 0-545-20410-0

12 11 10 9 8 7 6 5   13 14/0

Printed in the U.S.A.   40

First Scholastic printing, September 2009

Design by Richard Amari
Text set in Priska Serif and Celestia Adornado

Princess Alice. First to the palace.

Princess **Betty**. Still getting ready.

Princess **Criss**. Stealing a kiss.

Princess **Dot.** A lady she's not.

Princess **Elle**. Starting to yell.

Princess Flo. Waiting to go.

Princess **Grace**. Making a face.

Princess **Heather**, Dressed for the weath

Princess **Isabella**. Has no umbrella.

Princess Jane. Being a pain.

Princess **Kay**. Lost her way.

Princess Lori. Not in this story.

Princess Mandy. Ate too much candy.

Princess Nell, What is that smell?

Princess Olga. Dancing the polka.

Princess Pearl, The littlest girl.

Princess Quinn. Doesn't fit in.

Princess Ruth, Mithing a tooth.

Princess Sue. Not you, too!

Princess Tess. Couldn't care less.

Princess **Unice**. Why would she do this?

Princess Vikki. Very tricky.

Princess **Winnie**. Being a ninny.

Princess Xena. A true ballerina.

Princess Yvette. Isn't one, yet.

Princess Zaire. Finally there.

Put 'em all together
and what do you get?

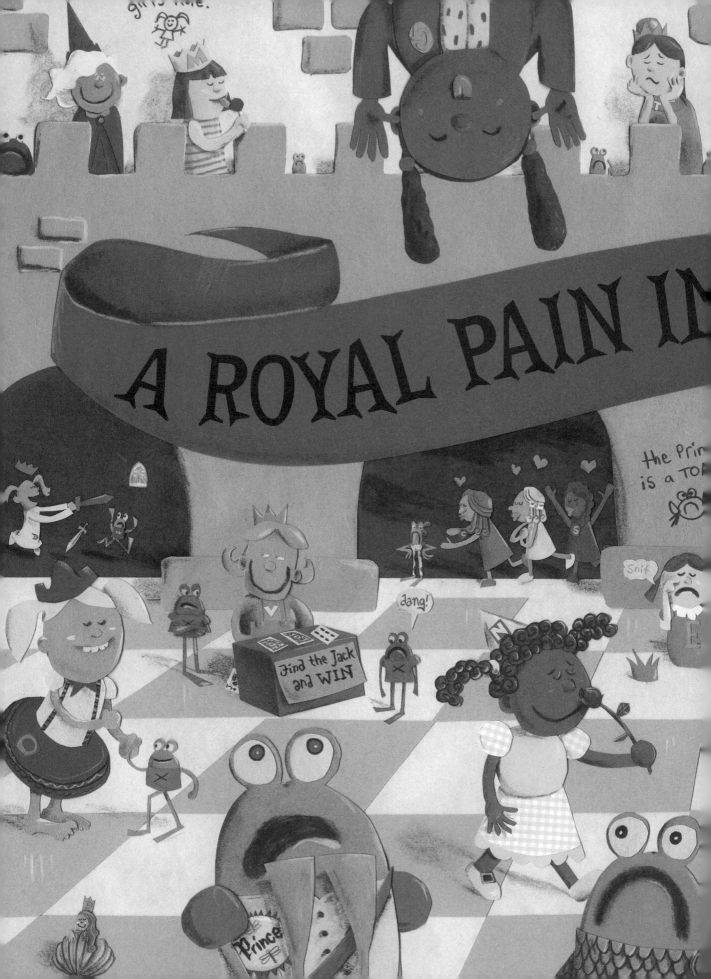

The End.